AMERiCA, I KNOW YOU

FREEDOM BOOK

A BILL MARTIN

BOWMAR

To my friend and colleague, Alan Heicklen

AMER¡CA,
I KNOW YOU

A FREEDOM BOOK BY BILL MARTIN JR.
WITH PAINTINGS BY TED RAND

America, I know you,
You're no stranger to me,

You are a bowlful of cherries,
You are the cherry tree,

You are a spoonful of honey on a slice of hot bread,

You are a nestful of hungry birds wanting to be fed,

You are a crowded grocery store with a revolving door,

You are an angry waterfall with an insistent roar,

You are a growling cement mixer churning the mix,

You are a man-made dream in a constant state of fix,

You are a color television with cameras on the moon,

You are a well-filled lunchbox gracing the noon,

You are a stinging teardrop splashing down my cheek,

You are the morning sunrise notching the mountain peak,

You are the pounding heartbeat of a hunted deer.

You are the ringing hope of a happy new year.